Max was purring loudly as he and Timmy walked home after the contest. 'Victory is in sight, my dear chap! Next week, that cup will be ours!'

Timmy wasn't so sure. 'You know who we're up against in the finals, don't you?'

'Yes, of course I do,' said Max. 'A place called HiTech House.'

'That's right,' said Timmy gloomily. 'HiTech House. They're all supposed to be geniuses, they train on computers . . .'

Timmy's school do really well in a national schools' quiz competition – until they meet HiTech House. When the HiTech team seem to get all the answers right – acting like robots – Timmy's magical cat, Max, decides to investigate . . .

Max and the Quiz Kids is the second title in a series about Timmy and his amazing magical cat from outer space, Max.

MAX AND THE QUIZ KIDS

MAX
and the
Quiz Kids

TERRANCE DICKS
ILLUSTRATED BY TONI GOFFE

YOUNG CORGI BOOKS

MAX AND THE QUIZ KIDS
A YOUNG CORGI BOOK 0 552 52722X

First published in Great Britain by
Piccadilly Press Ltd

PRINTING HISTORY
Piccadilly Press edition published 1990
Young Corgi edition published 1992

Text copyright © Terrance Dicks, 1990
Illustrations copyright © Toni Goffe, 1990

Young Corgi Books are published by Transworld Publishers Ltd, 61–63 Uxbridge Road, Ealing, London W5 5SA, in Australia by Transworld Publishers (Australia) Pty. Ltd, 15–23 Helles Avenue, Moorebank, NSW 2170, and in New Zealand by Transworld Publishers (N.Z.) Ltd, 3 William Pickering Drive, Albany, Auckland.

Made and printed in Great Britain by
Cox & Wyman Ltd, Reading, Berks.

Chapter One

Quiz Time

Max leaned back in his chair, studying the last question on the card. 'Who invented Mickey Mouse?' he drawled. 'Now, let me see . . .'

Timmy waited tensely. This was the last, vital question. If Max got this one right, he won the game.

The Tompkins family were having their Sunday night game of Trivial Pursuit. Timmy, his mum and dad, and Max, who was staying with the Tompkinses for a while.

Nothing unusual about that, you might think. Except that Max was a cat.

He'd arrived at the Tompkins' one dark and stormy night, and turned out to be a very unusual cat indeed.

He could talk, he could walk on his hind legs when he wanted to, and he seemed to have lots of mysterious magical powers. Above all Max had an air about him, a sort of natural, effortless, aristocratic superiority. Somehow you just knew that Max was a Very Important Person.

But for all his aristocratic air, Max liked to join into the Tompkins family life. He loved playing the quiz game and he nearly always won.

However, Entertainment wasn't Max's strongest subject and this time Timmy had hopes things might turn out differently. But not for long.

'Mickey Mouse,' said Max, 'was created

by the famous cartoonist and film maker
Walt Disney in 1928. The first Mickey
Mouse cartoon with sound, "Steamboat

Willie", was completed and shown in New York that same year . . . '

'All right, all right, Max, just "Walt Disney" will do,' said Timmy. 'You win, as usual!'

His mother went off to make the cocoa, while Timmy and his father tidied up the question cards and put the game back in its box. 'I sometimes think we waste too much time on this game,' grumbled Mr Tompkins.

Before Max's arrival, *he'd* usually been the winner.

'My dear Mr Tompkins, you mustn't say that,' protested Max. 'It's a splendid game, and most educational. I've learned a great deal from playing with you. It's been a real privilege.'

'Very kind of you, I'm sure,' said Mr Tompkins.

Timmy put the lid on the box and put it

back on the sideboard. 'Even my teacher thinks quizzes are educational, Dad. Our class is entering a team for the big Inter-Schools Quiz Championship this year. I don't suppose we'll win, but we hope to make it to the semi-finals.'

'You ought to get Max on your team,' said Mr Tompkins. 'You'd win then all right!'

Timmy's mother came back with the cocoa and they settled down to drink it.

'Tell me more about this Inter-Schools

Quiz of yours,' said Max. 'I find the whole idea very interesting . . .'

It was break-time the next day.

Timmy had just scored a brilliant goal between the two coats piled against the school wall when the goalie, a boy called Sam, shouted, 'A big black and white cat's just jumped over the wall.'

'Well, it'd better jump back then,' said Timmy, 'or the caretaker's dog will get it.' Then a worrying thought struck him. 'Did you say a black and white cat?'

He turned and saw Max, sitting by the bottom of the wall, looking with interest at the busy playground scene.

He also saw Killer, the caretaker's enormous dog, streaking murderously towards Max from the gatehouse.

Killer was a horrible dog, a huge vicious bull–mastiff who was usually kept on a chain. Mr Mallet, the caretaker, was a horrible man and he took a pride in Killer's

ferocity, boasting how many cats the big dog had 'seen off'.

'Look out, Max!' yelled Timmy. 'Run for it!'

Max turned and looked at the massive dog tearing towards him. But he didn't run.

Quite what he did do, Timmy was never really sure. Somehow Max seemed to *grow*, swelling from a big cat to something more like a full-grown panther.

He let out a ferocious howl. 'Raaarrow!'

Killer skidded to a halt.

Max stalked towards him, green eyes blazing. 'Raaarrow!'

Killer turned and fled, with Max bounding after him. There was a big old oak tree by the school gate and the big dog ran straight up the trunk and leaped into the fork of a branch where it crouched quivering.

Max, suddenly normal size again, looked up at the dog, yawned, and strolled away.

Mr Mallet dashed out of the gatehouse. 'What's going on? Where's Killer?'

Timmy pointed. 'Up there. I'm afraid my cat's just chased him up a tree!'

There was a tremendous fuss after that.

Mr Mallet went and got a ladder and tried to get Killer down. Killer struggled wildly, and three-quarters of the way down the ladder they both fell off.

Mr Mallet landed on top of Killer, who promptly bit him on the bottom. Mr Mallet yelled his head off and the first-aid lady had to be sent for . . .

The school enjoyed it all no end, and everyone was sorry when the bell rang and they had to go inside.

Timmy lost sight of Max after that and assumed he'd gone home.

The next period was history, with Mrs Maxwell, Timmy's class teacher, and at the end of it Mr Perkins, the art teacher, came in from the class next door. 'Anybody here know a cat called Max?'

Timmy put his hand up.

'Well, he's in my art class,' said Mr Perkins.

'I hope he's not upsetting the children,' said Mrs Maxwell.

'At the moment he's lecturing the class on the different ways of sketching with charcoal and painting in oils and watercolours. He says he's looking for someone called Timmy.'

'Send him in here,' said Mrs Maxwell. 'We're doing Shakespeare – perhaps he's an expert on that too?'

'Scarcely an expert, dear lady,' drawled Max, strolling into the classroom. 'But I think I may claim to have dabbled a little. A fascinating period . . .'

Next moment, Max was telling them all about life in Shakespeare's times. He told them how all the women's parts had to be played by boys because girls weren't allowed on stage, and how poor old Shakespeare had really been a sort of hired hack who had to churn out plays for the Queen and her court.

After the lesson, Mrs Maxwell and Max

had a long chat, and then Mrs Maxwell
called Timmy over. 'Your friend Max has
kindly offered to coach the class team for
the Inter-Schools Quiz. We'll start tonight
after school.'

Timmy looked at Max in amazement.
'Are you sure, Max?'

'Delighted to be of service, dear boy . . .'

There was no doubt about it, thought
Timmy, Max certainly had a way with
him. He was so relaxed and self-assured
that people accepted him without question
– just as Timmy and his family had done

when he first arrived.

Since Timmy lived very near school he could go home for lunch. On the way back he asked, 'Isn't it going to cause a bit of comment, Max, your coaching the team?'

'We'll tell everyone I'm your mascot,' said Max. 'After all, who's going to believe your winning team was coached by a cat!'

Chapter Two

Max Takes Charge

'How can we train for a general knowledge quiz?' asked Simon, the team captain, as they assembled in the classroom after school. 'I mean, it isn't like an exam, we don't even know the subjects, let alone the questions.'

'Simple,' said Max. 'The questions have got to be about something, haven't they?'

'Well, obviously,' snapped Simon.

Max beamed. 'There you are then. All you've got to do is learn everything about something, and something about everything and you're home and dry!'

That night, and every night after school for the rest of the week, Max put the team through a quick-fire question and answer session.

He fired question after question at them on every possible subject, supplying questions and answers from his own amazing memory.

The team worked hard, and it certainly paid off.

When the Quiz finally started, they won their first round with ease. Max kept up his coaching, and in the following weeks they won their next two rounds as well. Before they knew where they were, they were in the semi-final – and they won that too!

Max was purring proudly as he and Timmy walked home after the contest. 'Victory is in sight, my dear chap! Next week, that cup will be ours!'

Timmy wasn't so sure. 'You know who we're up against in the finals, don't you?'

'Yes, of course I do,' said Max. 'A place called HiTech House!'

'That's right,' said Timmy gloomily. 'HiTech House, a private school for the sons and daughters of the super-rich. They charge enormous fees and they've got all the latest teaching equipment. They're all supposed to be geniuses, they train on computers.'

Max didn't seem worried. 'The human mind can out-think any computer. I don't think you need worry about HiTech House. I've been studying them, you know.'

'You have?'

Max nodded. 'They're very bright, and they work hard, but they learn mostly about science and technology. This is a general knowledge quiz, remember. There are questions on books and paintings and geography and entertainment . . . all sorts of things. Your team has a much *wider* field of knowledge.'

'Well, they've been doing pretty well so far,' said Timmy.

HiTech House had skated through to the finals with ease, scoring even higher on average than Timmy's team.

The final was to be held in a special room in the local town hall, and there was a packed house when the two teams assembled on stage. The Mayor himself was acting as quiz master.

The HiTech team turned out to be rather a weird looking bunch. They arrived in a gleaming white van which they parked behind the town hall, and they all wore white suits and identical glasses with thick black frames and rims.

'I think we ought to ask for a blood test,' whispered Harry, the third member of Timmy's team. 'They look like robots to me!'

Robots or not, the HiTech team put up an amazing performance. They seemed to know the answer to every question, not only the ones about atoms and molecules but the capitals of South American states and the books of long-forgotten writers.

Science, art, history or whatever, the HiTech team knew the lot. They'd pause for a moment, as if thinking hard, then out would come the right answer in a flat monotonous voice.

Luckily Timmy's team were on top form as well, and they were only a few points behind at half-time.

'They're amazing,' whispered Timmy as he and his team sat sipping lemonade.

'Yes, but they're not quite perfect,'

Simon pointed out. 'They do get it wrong sometimes – luckily for us.'

'That's right,' said Harry. 'And sometimes it's the easiest questions they can't cope with . . .'

There was a flurry of movement on the other side of the room. Max had sprung into the lap of one of the HiTech team. The boy jumped up and tried to shove him away. For a moment Max clung on, then he jumped down and disappeared under the stage.

The contest resumed and the HiTech team kept up their amazing performance. It looked as if they were going to win easily. Then, just before the end, the public address system suddenly went wrong, giving out strange howling sounds.

Maybe this upset the HiTech lot, because they began making mistakes. Timmy's team pulled up level, then actually went into the lead . . .

The loudspeakers went on whining, and eventually the Mayor ordered them switched off.

'I'm afraid some vital wires have got misplaced and apparently they can't be replaced in time. If the audience will be good enough to keep very quiet and the teams will speak up, I'm sure we can manage.'

The end of the contest took place in a tense hush, and the HiTech team seemed to recover their form. The last question fell to them, and they were one point behind.

'If they get this wrong, we've won!' whispered Harry.

The Mayor read out the question. 'Who is the hero of Charles Dickens' first book – the one that made him famous?'

There was the usual pause, then the captain of the HiTech team said flatly, 'Mr Pickwick – and the book was called *Pickwick Papers*.'

'Correct!' said the Mayor, and there was a round of applause.

'Well, this is amazing,' said the Mayor. 'For the first time in the history of the contest, it has ended in a draw. Unfortunately we've run out of time and of questions, so I propose to ask both teams to come back for a rematch tomorrow night. I hope you'll all come back and watch what I'm sure will be a very exciting contest!'

That night Timmy was still too wound up to sleep – which was why he was still awake in the middle of the night. He saw a dark form slipping out of his bedroom window.

'Max?' he whispered. 'Where are you off to?'

'Oh, just off for a little prowl on the tiles, my dear fellow.'

Somehow the answer didn't ring true.

'Come on, Max, what are you up to?'

'If you must know, old boy, I'm about to pay a little visit to HiTech House.'

'Whatever for?'

'My whiskers have been twitching all evening,' said Max. 'In fact, you might say, I smell a HiTech rat!'

Chapter Three

Max on the Prowl

'Up you come,' whispered Max.

He reached down a paw, and somehow Timmy found himself whisked to the top of the high wall surrounding HiTech House.

Unable to talk Max out of his mission, Timmy had insisted on going with him.

He jumped down inside the grounds and Max landed silently beside him.

'What now?' asked Timmy.

Max pointed to the dark shape of the

building looming ahead of them – dark, that is, except for lighted windows here and there.

'People live here, you know,' said Timmy. 'And scientists work all round the clock. There'll be people about.'

'Don't worry, old chap, just leave it to me,' said Max confidently.

They moved across the lawn and into the shadow of the building.

'I bet there'll be guard dogs,' said Timmy.

No sooner were the words out of his mouth than he was proved right.

To his horror he saw two lean black shapes racing towards them across the lawn.

Compared to these two, poor old Killer was just a kitten. These were trained guard dogs, attack dogs, the SAS of the dog world. Not even Max was going to chase these two up a tree.

To Timmy's amazement, Max sat down and began to purr.

The two dogs raced up to them, stopping short within springing distance.

'Max, look!' gasped Timmy.

'I see them,' said Max. 'Just keep perfectly still, we don't want to frighten them.'

Max went on purring, a deep hypnotic sound.

The two dogs cocked their heads.

Then they too sat down.

Then they stretched out, heads on their paws.

They yawned, they stretched, and very soon they were fast asleep. They growled slowly and twitched in their sleep, giving little excited whines.

'What are they doing?' whispered Timmy.

'Dreaming, old boy. They're just enjoying a nice day's hunting on the

African plains.' Max looked up at the building. 'No point in you coming in, you stay here on guard. I shan't be long.'

Before Timmy had time to protest, Max streaked up the nearest drainpipe and disappeared through an open window on the second floor.

Timmy was left on guard. 'Though what I'm supposed to be guarding,' he thought, 'I've no idea. Max is inside the building, too far away to hear any warning. I suppose he just wanted me out of the way.'

Timmy huddled into the shadows. 'Suppose the dogs wake up, and decide *I'm* whatever they think they're hunting? They might eat me before they realise their mistake!'

Black clouds sailed past the moon, trees and bushes rustled and an owl hooted mournfully.

Timmy stepped back and looked up at the open window. 'Suppose the man in charge of the dogs comes to find out what's happened to them? There must be humans as well as dogs on guard . . . '

Once again, Timmy was proved right. A huge hand clamped down on his shoulder and a voice breathed, 'Gotcha!'

Timmy twisted round and saw an enormous man with an enormous moustache. He wore a police-type uniform with a shiny peaked cap and there were gold sergeant's stripes on his sleeve.

'Gotcha!' said the Sergeant again, his moustache whiffling in the moonlight. 'I won't ask what you're doing here, lad, 'cos I know! This building is packed with valuable scientific gubbins, and you're the lookout for a gang of thieves.' He looked at the sleeping dogs. 'Drug the dogs, move in and clear it all out, is that the idea? Well, you didn't reckon with me, Sonny Jim, because I've gotcha! And when your mates come out, I'll get them as well.'

Suddenly a black shape dropped softly from the darkness above. Max rose up on his hind legs, green eyes glowing, purring that deep, hypnotic purr.

'Good evening, Constable,' he drawled. 'Everything all right?'

For a moment the Sergeant just stared at him. Then, still gripping Timmy with his left hand, he crashed to attention. 'Everything's in order, Inspector. I've checked all the doorways on my beat.'

'Jolly good, well done . . . What have you got there?'

'Street-urchin, Inspector, found him skulking in the alley behind the shops. Little perishers will pinch anything not nailed down.'

'Might as well throw the poor little beggar back, Constable. Too small for the frying pan, eh what?'

To Timmy's relief, the Sergeant released his grip. 'Off you go, you little imp. Thank your stars the Inspector came along. Hurry, now!'

Timmy ducked back into the shadows.

'Carry on, Constable,' said Max.

'Yessir!' said the Sergeant and he marched off round the corner. Timmy came out of the shadows. 'Crickey! Where does he think he is?'

'Back on the beat when he was a young Police Constable, I imagine.'

'Will he be all right?'

'Oh yes, he'll wake up soon, just like the dogs. None of them will remember that anything's happened.'

'What were you up to in there?'

Cool as ever, Max strolled back towards the wall. 'Just pottering about, old boy. Paid a little visit to their communications laboratory. Fascinating place . . .'

'Did you find out anything interesting?'

'You'll know tomorrow evening,' promised Max. 'And so will our too-clever friends on the HiTech team . . .'

Chapter Four

The Showdown

Whatever Max had discovered, it didn't make any difference to the first part of the replay.

Nothing had changed at all.

The HiTech team turned up in their big white van, still wearing their white suits and their heavy black-rimmed glasses.

They were still as boring and as brilliant as ever, hesitating for a moment, then droning out the correct answer to every question. Timmy's team had to fight hard to keep level with them, and by half-time they were actually a couple of points behind.

'We're still in with a chance,' said Harry bravely. 'If only they have another little collapse.'

'No sign of it so far,' said Simon. 'They're performing like robots.'

Max rubbed against Timmy's ankles.

Timmy bent down to stroke him, and Max whispered in his ear.

Timmy straightened up. 'I think I'll pop outside for a moment, get a breath of air to clear my head.'

'Don't be late,' warned Simon. 'Remember, everything depends on this last round.'

Max led Timmy to the car park at the back of the town hall. He whispered more instructions and Timmy nodded and picked him up. With Max in his arms, Timmy went over to the gleaming white

HiTech van and rapped on the front window.

After a moment the window wound down and a face appeared. It wore thick-rimmed black glasses and looked exactly like the HiTech team members inside. 'Yes?'

'Is this your cat?' asked Timmy. 'I found it wandering and – '

'No,' said the man flatly and started to wind the window up.

Max leaped from Timmy's arms and disappeared through the narrowing gap.

There were outraged yells from inside and then silence – followed by the sound of purring . . .

Still following Max's instructions, Timmy turned and hurried back into the town hall.

Simon was already starting to panic. 'Come on Timmy, where have you been? We're just about to start . . . '

The first question was for Timmy's team, one about old movies. 'Who played Sam Spade in the first film of "The Maltese Falcon?"

This last round was all team questions so you were allowed to help each other. 'Humphrey Bogart,' whispered Simon.

Timmy shook his head. 'It's a trick question. Bogart was in the third version.' He raised his voice. 'An actor called Ricardo Cortez, in 1931.'

'Correct!' said the Mayor and everyone cheered.

He turned to the HiTech team. 'Who was the first president of the United States?'

'Donald Duck,' said the HiTech captain. There was an astonished silence.

'Wrong,' said the Mayor. 'The answer of course is George Washington.'

Another question for Tim's team. What was the capital of Peru? They got it right – Lima – and he turned back to HiTech. 'Who is the heavyweight champion of the world?'

'Paul McCartney,' said one of the HiTech team.

This time there was a definite ripple of laughter.

'Wrong!'

After that, things just went from bad to worse.

It scarcely mattered that Tim's team got most of their questions right.

The HiTech team got every single one
of theirs wrong!

They said Madonna invented the
telephone, and Mrs Thatcher starred in
'Gone with the Wind'.

They seemed to think the capital of
Poland was Hong Kong, the population of
China was forty-seven and Kylie Minogue
was Prime Minister of Great Britain.

The easier the questions, the sillier their answers, and when the round was over, Timmy's team had won by twenty-one points.

'Well,' said the Mayor. 'After a most amazing finish, the winners are . . . '

Before he could finish, the HiTech team jumped up, shoved rudely past him, and ran from the stage.

Timmy hurried after them. He wanted
to see what happened, and besides, he was
worried about Max.

The HiTech team dashed straight round
to the car park and headed for their van.

Just before they reached it, the door
opened and Max jumped out.

Ignoring him, the team jumped straight
into their van and slammed the door
behind them.

From inside the van came the sound of thumps and yells, and soon the whole van started to rock.

'Sounds like some sort of a brawl,' said Max. 'How sordid! Let's go and collect our cup, shall we?'

Chapter Five

Max Explains

The cup was presented to Timmy's team amidst tremendous applause, and Max got a special clap for being their mascot. That night the team went round to Timmy's house for a celebration supper, and when the meal was over everyone turned to Max. 'Speech! Speech!' they called.

'Come on Max,' said Timmy. 'Tell us what's been going on!'

Max settled back in his chair. 'Well, I was a bit suspicious of those HiTech chaps

at the quiz final – the first one, I mean.
The mechanical way they trotted out the
answers, the way they seemed to know
absolutely everything about such a huge
range of subjects. They were just too good
to be true. And then there was the way
they looked . . . '

'I thought they were all robots,' said
Harry.

'So did I for a while,' said Max
seriously. 'But I jumped on one of the
team's lap and dug in. He was flesh and
blood all right!'

'It was those big black glasses, wasn't
it?' said Timmy. 'I always felt there was
something dodgy about the glasses.'

'Exactly,' said Max. ' A touch of the old
double bluff. The glasses and the white
suits – they were so noticeable it was
obvious they were meant to hide
something. So I performed a little
experiment. Remember when the public

address system went wrong? Well, that
was me!'

'I remember,' said Simon. 'The HiTech
lot went all to pieces. I thought the noise
was bothering them.'

'So it was – though not in the way you
might think. Later on that night, I paid an
unofficial visit to their communications lab
and got a look at their secret designs.'

'So they were using radio,' said Timmy. 'That's why they couldn't answer when the PA was howling. The static jammed their transmissions!'

'Exactly,' said Max. 'The glasses were disguised headphones, and they had a small but powerful radio transmitter in their van. They also had a team of experts and a man with a set of encyclopedias to look up the answers. Sometimes there was interference anyway, and they got the odd question wrong.'

'So what happened tonight?' asked
Harry.

Max tried to look modest. 'Oh, nothing
to it, really. I popped into their van during
the interval and, er, persuaded them to let
me take over the answer-giving. Afraid I
rather messed it up for them!'

'You certainly did,' said Timmy. 'So
that's why the team rushed out and
thumped the people in the van!'

'They did seem a bit put out, didn't
they?' agreed Max. 'Still, serves them
right, cheats never prosper – at least, they
shouldn't do.'

Simon raised his glass to Max. 'Well,
here's to you, Max. You coached us
through to the finals and saved us from the
cheats.'

'To Max!' said everyone and raised their
glasses.

If it wasn't for his fur Max would have

blushed. 'Not at all, happy to be of service.' He put a paw on Timmy's shoulder. 'I'm finding life with the Tompkins family *very* educational!'

MAGNIFICENT MAX

BY TERRANCE DICKS
ILLUSTRATED BY TONI GOFFE

'There's something very unusual about Max, you know . . .'

There certainly *is* something very unusual about Max, the mysterious black and white cat Timmy finds in the garden on the night of the great storm. For one thing he can talk. He can also walk on his hind legs, eat with a knife and fork and he has the most exquisite manners.

Timmy and Max quickly become friends and Timmy knows that he wants Max to stay, especially when he discovers that Max has some very unusual talents – magical talents. But who is Max? Where has he come from? Timmy is determined to find out . . .

From the author of the popular *T.R. Bear* series.

0 552 52610 X

YOUNG
CORGI

T.R. BEAR: ENTER T.R.

BY TERRANCE DICKS

It all started when Jimmy got a parcel from his Uncle Colin in America. The teddy bear inside was unlike any bear Jimmy had ever seen. He looked tough, and he was wearing glasses! According to the label, his name was Theodore Roosevelt – T.R. for short.

Jimmy soon finds out that life with T.R. Bear is quite eventful . . .

SBN 0 552 52301 1

T.R. BEAR:
T.R.'s HALLOWE'EN

BY TERRANCE DICKS
ILLUSTRATED BY SUSAN HELLARD

From ghoulies and ghosties,
and long-leggety Beasties,
And things that go BUMP in the night . . .

It's Hallowe'en again and, as usual, T.R. is right in the middle of all the excitement. Dressed in a horrifying demon-mask and a red cloak, he sets out trick or treating with Jimmy and his brother and sister.

Jimmy has a nasty feeling that T.R. might get a little over-excited and he's right! For T.R. persuades him to go and call at old Mrs Maltby's spooky house and suddenly Jimmy is in big trouble. And it's all T.R.'s fault . . .

This is the fifth hilarious tale of T.R. Bear and his adventures.

SBN 0 552 52507 3

YOUNG
CORGI